Taking Off

Taking Off

Memories of de Havilland at Hatfield

Assembled from a variety of sources by
Hatfield Local History Society

Edited by G. Philip Marris

Published March 2016

Published by Hatfield Local History Society
Printed via www.lulu.com
Copyright © 2016 – Hatfield Local History Society

ISBN 978-0-9928416-5-2

COVER PHOTOGRAPH

DH 98 Mosquito – twin-engine fighter and bomber (from a 1945
de Havilland advertisement)

FOREWORD

THE history of the de Havilland Aircraft Company is well documented with many books written on the subject.

This publication tells the story of de Havilland through the eyes of some of those who were there at the time. The story starts in the early 1930s when the company first moved to Hatfield and continues through World War II and into the 1950s.

Personal recollections by their nature are not always accurate, especially when committed to paper sometimes years after the event. Readers will therefore find occasional editorial comments within the running text. These are given in *italics* within square brackets. Grammatical corrections have also been made but with a hopefully light touch that doesn't distort the original voices.

It was beyond the scope of this small volume to recall everything, for example the trials and tribulations of the DH 106 Comet jet airliner. Nor does this book cover the post-1960 era by which time de Havilland had been absorbed into Hawker Siddeley.

Thanks are expressed to Mill Green Museum, BAE Systems and Aviation Ancestry for providing access to their respective archives. Thanks are also due to the individuals whose personal recollections of de Havilland have provided such a rich source of material for this book.

Amongst the team who have undertaken this work are: Albert Jackson, former employee of de Havilland; Christine Martindale, chairman of Hatfield Local History Society; Hazel K. Bell who created the index; and G. Philip Marris who edited the work.

LONDON AEROPLANE
CLUB ★ ★ ★ HATFIELD

A FLYING TRAINING CENTRE SECOND TO NONE

Initial and advanced instruction. Aerobatics, blind-flying, navigation. Large fleet, latest single and multi-engined, open and closed aircraft, Tiger Moth, Hornet Moth, Dragonfly. Restaurant, tennis, squash, swimming pool, etc.

SERIOUS TUITION IN AN ATMOSPHERE OF LEISURE

CONTENTS

UNDER 15 FLAGS

Tiger Moths have been selected for the comprehensive flying training of pilots of the Military and Naval Aviation Services of no less than fifteen nations.

TIGER MOTH
Military and Marine Training Aircraft

Manufactured by

THE DE HAVILLAND AIRCRAFT CO., LTD.
HATFIELD AERODROME, HATFIELD, HERTFORDSHIRE

ILLUSTRATIONS

Unless otherwise indicated, photographs and advertisements in this book are the intellectual property, respectively, of BAE Systems or Aviation Ancestry. Grateful thanks are expressed to both organisations for providing these images and permitting their use.

Chapter 1   Hatfield's Irony

This article was written by Peter Kingsford in October 1995 and published by Hatfield Local History Society in its March 1996 (Issue 20) newsletter. It recalls Hatfield's transition from the aircraft industry to becoming a University town.

HATFIELD town suffers under the irony of change. Until a few years ago the aircraft industry was by far the biggest employer. Now that role falls to the University of Hertfordshire.

Such a change is not new to the town. Early in the twentieth century, the Great Northern Railway with its locomotive depot was the biggest and most stable employer. That faded with the railway amalgamation of 1920. But this contemporary change has an ironic twist, for the first major employer gave way to the second which arose from it.

The de Havilland Aircraft Company settled in Hatfield in 1934. Only sixty years later, under different ownership, it has given way to the University as the big employer. De Havilland grew, particularly during the 1939-45 war, so that Hatfield was in danger of becoming a one-industry town. The firm, after great successes but undergoing changes in ownership as successively part of Hawker Siddeley and British Aerospace, grew in a town of not more than some 25,000. Many, if not most, employees lived in Hatfield. Much house-building took place to accommodate them. This development reached a climax when the Hatfield Development Corporation began to build Hatfield New Town in 1951 when many of the new houses went to employees of de

1

Havilland. The effect was to produce prosperity but now Hatfield was dependent even more on one industry.

By 1952, the local aircraft industry had reached a peak of employment. That year also saw the opening of Hatfield Technical College. The college arose where it did because of de Havilland. The site of ninety acres of farmland was a personal gift from the chairman of the company, A. S. Butler, to the County Council in May 1944. The college library was named after him.

Butler's condition for the gift was that the work of the de Havilland Aeronautical Technical School, established in 1928, be conducted by the new college. This was a bonus for the college for it meant that it could start in 1952 with some advanced courses – those for the examination of the Royal Aeronautical Society among others.

Aeronautical engineering thus became the flagship of the college for some years. When the college opened it had some fifty employees, including thirty lecturers.

Alan Samuel Butler J.P. (1898-1987)

As the college rapidly diversified, de Havilland, though the major industrial connection, became only one of many firms locally with college students. There was a big increase in chemistry, biology, electronics, business studies and computer studies. This accelerated when degrees of the Council for National Academic Awards in those subjects could be conferred from the early 1960s. Employment by

2

the college increased in line with these requirements. For instance, a single librarian in 1952 eventually became half-a-dozen. By that time Hawker Siddeley had absorbed de Havilland.

Earlier, the company had initiated and developed jet airliners and had overcome the Comet disaster of 1954. Then, at the time that the college, renamed the College of Technology, was developing half-a-dozen degree courses of its own, scores of Tridents were being built, all at Hatfield. Employment rose considerably in both organisations. By the 1970s, when the college had become a poly-technic, the aircraft firm had been nationalised as British Aerospace and was still the biggest employer in

Hatfield College of Technology

the town. But this had not many years to go. For, whereas, in June 1992, the polytechnic had blossomed into the University of Hertfordshire, the closure of the aircraft firm, now privatised, would be announced only three months later. While the gradual cessation of employment in aircraft took place until December 1993, the university now became the chief employer in Hatfield.

Geoffrey de Havilland with homemade motorbike (c.1903)

Founders of the de Havilland Aircraft Company:
(L to R standing) Francis St. Barbe and Wilfred
E. Nixon; (seated) Charles C. Walker, Geoffrey
de Havilland and Frank Hearle.

4

Chapter 2   How it All Began

This article was written by Abi Wilson while studying at the University of Hertfordshire. It was published on the "Our Hatfield" web site in March 2011.

S IR Geoffrey de Havilland was born on 27th July, 1882 near High Wycombe, Buckinghamshire. It was expected that, at the age of seventeen, Geoffrey would train for the clergy. However, his interest in mechanics overshadowed previous expectations and Geoffrey went on to train at the Crystal Palace Engineering School in 1900. The school provided Geoffrey with knowledge of mechanical engineering and with this he built his own motorcycle.

Sir Geoffrey de Havilland

After three years, he gained an apprenticeship at Willans & Robinson in Warwickshire and in 1905 became a draughtsman at the Wolseley Tool & Motor Car Company at Adderley Park in Birmingham. After working for the Daimler Motor Company, Geoffrey's brother Ivon designed the Iris car which was manufactured at Willesden, London. Ivon introduced Geoffrey to a number of people who would help him in his future.

5

Inspired by Wilbur Wright in 1908, Geoffrey de Havilland knew that his future would revolve around aviation. With financial aid from his maternal grandfather, Geoffrey started to design his first aeroplane. Although his first aeroplane was unsuccessful, his second took flight in 1910. The plane was bought by the British Army's balloon factory at Farnborough and de Havilland was given a job as a pilot and aircraft designer.

At the end of the First World War, Geoffrey set up the de Havilland Aircraft Company with the help of former colleagues. The most successful product to come out of this company was the Moth series of biplanes.

In 1934, the de Havilland Comet Racer won a race from London to Melbourne in under seventy-one hours. In the following year, the company pioneered the British manufacture of American controllable-pitch propellers, which would become crucial in winning the Battle of Britain.

At the outbreak of the Second World War, the company was manufacturing the Tiger Moth and Dragon Rapide biplanes, soon to be joined by the Mosquito monoplane. The Tiger Moth, which was first sold in 1931, was predominantly used for the Royal Air Force to train new pilots during the Second World War.

In 1946, Geoffrey de Havilland Jnr was partaking in a test flight when the aircraft broke up near Gravesend in Kent. The death of Geoffrey Jnr not only affected his family but also the entirety of the company. Geoffrey Snr's youngest son, John, also died in an air collision. It was shortly after this that Geoffrey's wife passed away.

In 1960, the de Havilland group was acquired by Hawker Siddeley and Geoffrey's role within the company diminished. Geoffrey carried on flying planes long after his retirement but sadly died in 1965 of a cerebral haemorrhage.

Geoffrey de Havilland was awarded an OBE in 1918, a CBE in 1934 and he received the Air Force Cross in 1919. He was knighted in 1944 and appointed to the Order of Merit in 1962.

This article was written by Don Lawrence and published by Hatfield Local History Society in 2007. Don Lawrence was born in Hatfield in 1914 and attended St. Audrey's School until 1930 when he joined the de Havilland School of Flying as a trainee ground engineer. He obtained A and C Licences for Tiger Moth airframes and Gipsy Major engines.

IN the 1920s my father and uncle, who were agricultural contractors at Hatfield, secured a contract to do drainage, remove hedges and prepare the site to build an aerodrome for the de Havilland Aircraft Company on Sinclair's Farm, adjacent to the Barnet Bypass, to be ready by 1930.

At that time, the de Havilland School of Flying was operating from the Company's aerodrome at Stag

London Flying Club at Hatfield, 1930
(swimming pool, clubhouse and service hangers)

Lane, Edgware, but the increasing housing development had made the company look for an alternative location. After flying over

7

several different areas by Gipsy Moth, a site at Hatfield seemed to be the best choice and a satisfactory deal was done with the owner.

The first hangar to be erected was for the Flying School, later extended to accommodate the Service Department and the London Aeroplane Club. The restaurant was built at the same time as the Flying School, and the swimming pool [*and squash courts*] later.

During the course of his construction work, my father had come into contact with Bob Hardingham. Bob had been Chief Engineer of the Flying School at Stag Lane and, in 1930, had moved to Hatfield in the same capacity. My father asked if there was a vacancy for a young lad and that is how I became the first Hatfield person to work for de Havilland at Hatfield; all the other employees came out every day from Edgware. Bob had one of the first MGs, which was really a Bullnose Morris with an MG badge, top speed 50 mph. The ground staff consisted of four ground engineers, two aerodrome labourers (whose job it was to swing the propellers for starting and also to keep the aircrafts clean), a labourer to keep the hangar clean and make the tea, and myself as a trainee ground engineer. R.W. Reeve was the Chief Flying Instructor and there were four other flying instructors, all ex-pilots from the 1914/18 War. Rivers-Oldmeadow gave instruction in navigation and it was something to see him jump, with his one leg, over the side of his open-top Bentley and drive off.

DH 60 Moth - two-seater biplane

The aircraft fleet consisted of five DH 9Js and four Gipsy Moths. This was the Flying School when I joined in June 1930.

My job was cleaning the sparking plugs used in the Gipsy and DH 9J Jaguar radial engines, washing down the engines after the day's flying and helping with routine maintenance. Very often before flying started, farm livestock which had broken through the fences of adjoining fields had to be rounded up.

Most of the flying was for training of pilots for the RAF Reserve. There was also a Stage and Screen Flying Club where well known "Stars" of the day came to Hatfield to fly, one of whom was Ralph Richardson who later had his own Gipsy Moth which was garaged in the aircraft lock-ups at Hatfield.

Ralph Richardson in his DH 60 Moth, 1927

The near location of Elstree to Hatfield made the choice easy when it came to films requiring aircraft and many films were made here including *Bulldog Drummond*, *The Flying Fool* and one which starred Jack Buchanan. One of the flying instructors would double for the leading man. Life was so laid-back in those days that everything stopped for film making.

When the restaurant opened, managed by Mrs. Reeve, wife of the Chief Flying Instructor, it attracted many weekend visitors who flew in and gave it a Country Club atmosphere. An area was fenced off next to the swimming pool for the general public to watch the flying.

A number of pilots from the First World War, who were on the Reserve, were required to fly a certain amount of hours. One of these veterans took off on a cross-country flight in a DH 9J and was away all day with no news of him. Late in the evening, an aircraft shot up the aerodrome and then did a terrible landing. After taxiing in, the pilot climbed out of the cockpit and fell over, blind drunk. He had spent all day visiting old colleagues in their Officers' Mess. One of these wartime pilots owned a Moth and also an SE 5[1] which he would fly occasionally.

John Tranum, the parachutist, used Hatfield to train for the world's longest delayed drop. Tranum and the pilot both used oxygen on these flights. On the official flight, having reached the altitude required, the pilot informed Tranum but could not get any response. On landing, Tranum was found dead in the cockpit due to failure of his oxygen supply.

One DH 9J[2] crashed at Hatfield in 1932 and the rest were scrapped in 1933. The 9Js were replaced with ten Tiger Moths starting with G-ACDA. Two Gipsy Moths were retained for the RAF Flying Club.

DH 9 Single engine bomber biplane

Bob Hardingham left in 1934 to join the Air Ministry, later transferring to the Air Registration Board where he became head man and, after the 1939/45 War, he was knighted for his service to aviation. Everyone got on with Bob and I was sorry to see him go. The day he left, he gave me his tool chest which I still have.

---

[1] The Royal Aircraft Factory SE 5 was a British biplane fighter aircraft of the First World War.

[2] DH 9J was a modernised and re-engined version of the DH 9 used by the de Havilland School of Flying.

Sid Weedon, who started with the Company in 1921, was promoted to Chief Engineer. In 1927, Sid with another engineer built the first Gipsy engine.

The nearby Service Department provided more interest. Mollison's Puss Moth "Hearts Content" in which he was the first to fly solo in 1932 on an east-to-west transatlantic flight, made an appearance. In 1933 Jim Mollison and Amy Johnson, now his wife, flew the Atlantic in the DH 84 Dragon "Seafarer". Unfortunately at the end of the flight they crashed. The wreckage was brought back to the Service Department and repaired.

1933 also saw a young New Zealander, Jean Batten, embarking on record-breaking flights, starting with a DH 60 Moth. She carried on these flights until 1937, the last being in a Percival Gull. The last time I saw her was when she brought the Gull into the Service Department for a top overhaul of the Gipsy Six engine.

In 1934 there was a rumour that a secret racing monoplane was being built in the recently erected adjacent aircraft factory. This was confirmed when we saw test pilot Hubert Broad flying the Comet racer. Three were built for the England to Australia Air Race, one of which, "Grosvenor House", was to win.

DH 88 Comet twin-engine racing monoplane

Life for me was full of interest and I was always "up at the drome" in my spare time. The Flying School became No. 1 Elementary and Reserve Flying Training School in 1935 (although

11

still referred to by the staff as "The Flying School") and a scheme for training Short Service Commission pilots was introduced.

Flying Instructors wore de Havilland uniforms while the ground staff wore white flying overalls with a DH badge on the left pocket.

R.W. Reeve left Hatfield in November 1935 to take charge as Chief Flying Instructor of a new DH-owned Flying School (No 13 E & R.F.T.S) at White Waltham. C.A. Pike, one of the instructors, became Chief Flying Instructor at Hatfield.

As most instructors were ex-RAF, due respect had to be paid as the school was very much RAF-orientated. Some instructors had nicknames but these were for fellow officers not the ordinary ground staff.

Capt. R. W. Reeve with his pupil the Duchess of Bedford at Stag Lane, 1928

1936 saw the first SBAC [*Society of British Aircraft Constructors*] Show at Hatfield. The Flying School hangar was cleared, the aircraft being picketed on the aerodrome. Beck & Pollitzer transformed the hangar into an exhibition hall for the display of engines and components. Twenty-eight aircraft were in the afternoon flying display which included the Spitfire and Hurricane. The public were not admitted to this one-day event.

Such was the success of this event, in 1937 it became a two-day show. Forty aircraft were on display, thirty taking part in the flying, including the new DH Albatross four-engine airliner.

The star of the show was the Short Empire Flying Boat "Calpurnia" which did several low flights across the aerodrome. Again the public were not admitted and this was to be the last SBAC Show until it resumed at Radlett in 1946.

The RAF Flying Club's Gipsy Moths were sold and replaced by Hornet Moths G-ADIS and G-ADMN. G-ADIS came with tapered main-planes; these were removed and the later type fitted. Tiger Moth G-ADSI which followed at a later date crashed in Scotland and was written off. Two Moth Minors joined the Club in 1939.

1937 was a sad year for de Havilland when their Chief Test Pilot, Bob Waight, was killed while practising for an attempt on the 100 Km Record in TK4, G-AETK, a small racing monoplane built by the DH Technical School. Bob Waight had been a Ground Engineer at Stag Lane before becoming a Test Pilot.

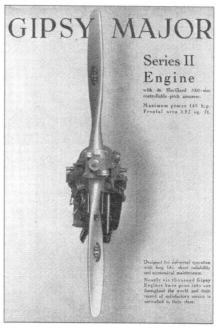

Another fatal accident occurred in January 1938 when, during low cloud, a Flying School Tiger Moth G-ADHW collided with a Gloster Gauntlet and crashed near Smallford, killing the three pilots.

By now I was a Licensed Ground Engineer, having A and C licences covering the Tiger Moth airframe and Gipsy Major engine.

de Havilland advertisement, 1937

With the increase in RAF training, Hawker Harts and Audax aircraft for advanced training were added to the school fleet and, in

13

February 1938, we moved into a new hangar when two Avro Ansons and three Fairey Battles arrived. With the prospect of more Tiger Moths, it was obvious the new building was not large enough and an extension was added in 1939. More staff – mostly ex-RAF personnel – were employed.

Alex Henshaw won the 1938 Kings Cup in his Mew Gull G-AEXF. Naturally I had a ringside seat at all of these events.

A Volunteer Reserve pilot flying an Audax and supposed to be on "circuits and bumps", crashed on houses at Edmonton, North London. The aircraft caught fire and twelve people were killed, including the pilot; it was a mystery why he was there.

The Audax aircraft did not have dual control and had to be air-tested by an instructor prior to the day's flying before being handed over to a pupil. This gave plenty of opportunity for a member of the ground staff to have a flight standing in the rear gunner's cockpit. How long the flight lasted depended on who the pilot was; with some it was only a quick flip round the aerodrome.

Starting in 1939, night-flying circuits and landings were carried out on Friday nights with the dual-control Hawker Harts. At sunset, a flare path would be laid out using paraffin gooseneck flares. An old Humber Snipe motor car with the back seat removed was used as transport. During flying, an ambulance and fire truck stood by, the latter being an in-house conversion from a car into a truck, its open body containing several large fire extinguishers. One of the engineers was the driver. I cannot remember anyone being given any formal training in the use of this equipment. Just prior to the war, a fire engine suitable for aerodrome use was acquired. Night flying finished about 1am.

At this time, a two-shift system was in operation – 7am until 10pm every day, including Saturday and Sunday. The only overtime was night-flying, approximately three hours. As we were salaried staff, which obviously suited the Company, overtime was paid at a flat rate, not premium rate as would have been paid for working Saturday, Sunday and unsocial hours if we had been

14

hourly paid. No doubt the Flying School employees would have benefited by a large amount if they had not been salaried staff. Whether sick pay, holiday pay and free overalls compensated for this is doubtful. Very few people complained about the odd working hours or took advantage of sick pay, although a doctor's note was required after two days.

Licensed Ground Engineers were paid £5 per week, plus 10/- for every extra licence acquired. Aerodrome staff received £3.

There were few crashes considering the number of hours flown; the aircraft would fly continually from 8am until sunset, weather permitting, seven days a week. Incidents such as aircraft being tipped on their noses or onto their backs were usually due to inexperienced pupil pilots.

Although Chamberlain had flown to Germany in 1938 and received a piece of paper from Hitler saying, "Peace Sure", not many believed this and, as 1939 progressed, more signs of preparation for war became evident with buildings being camouflaged and protected with sandbags.

The Harts, Audaxs and Ansons left for an unknown destination in August. The Battles took off immediately after war was declared on the 3rd September. One returned; the pilot forgot to lower the undercarriage and did a wheels-up landing – surely the first crash of the war.

With the announcement of War, an era had

Amy Johnson CBE (1903-41) with Gipsy Moth

ended. No more to be seen were the likes of Amy Johnson, Jim

15

Mollison, Jean Batten and the rest of the record-breakers who had been frequent visitors to Hatfield in between their worldwide flights as members of the Flying Club, but many became members of the Air Transport Auxiliary (ATA), ferrying new, damaged and repaired war planes between maintenance depots and service aerodromes. It was on such service that Amy Johnson was drowned in the Thames estuary after baling out while off-course in bad weather in January 1941. Nor were we to see the budding aircraft-makers with their light aircraft: Chiltern; Comper Swift; Dart Kitten; and the Drone powered glider. Some had entered National races and been successful.

In those grim days at the beginning of the war, few could have predicted the advances that aircraft would make before the end of war – the design of the peacetime Comet racer and construction of the Albatross were the forerunners to the success of the Mosquito – or how the gas turbine engine would revolutionize future aircraft design and travel. Who could have visualised the empire that de Havilland would build after the precarious days of 1920?

After leaving Hatfield, little or nothing was heard of the pilots who trained at No. 1 EFTS but over the years, information trickled through that many had become high-ranking officers: Wing Commanders; Group Captains; an Air Chief Marshall; and a Rear Admiral. Sadly one who trained under the Short Service Commission Scheme in 1936 was captured after the "Great Escape" from a German prisoner of war camp and shot on Hitler's orders.

No. 1 EFTS was located at Panshanger during and after the war. It closed down on 31st March, 1953 having been a Flying School for thirty years. Before then, I had moved on to being an inspector on larger and more modern aeroplanes.

When I look back, I appreciate that those years working at the Flying School were the most enjoyable of my time in aviation.

Chapter 4   My First Flight (1939)

This article was first published in the de Havilland (Hatfield) Club Magazine, September 1939. Fred Clark, a young lad of 14, wrote down these excellent impressions shortly after experiencing his first flight, piloted by Mr. Pike, chief instructor of the de Havilland School of Flying.

THE machine which I was going up in was a Hornet Moth, a two-seat cabin biplane. Getting into it was like getting into a car. No fuss, but care had to be taken not to step on the fabric of the wing.

We taxied for a long time, bumping continuously, and finally turned into the wind and waited until everything was clear. Then the motor took up a stronger note and the plane started moving faster. Soon, with a last big bump, the machine became air-borne, and all bumps ceased.

DH 87 Hornet Moth

The climb was fairly fast and I saw the men working on a new building gradually seem to change their shape and position. Seen

17

18

from above, they looked as if they were leaning backwards, and sticking their feet forwards.

A few seconds after this, I looked at the altimeter and saw that we were up to four hundred feet. Things looked fairly small from that height, but four hundred feet for an aeroplane is low, very low. Still, the roads, fields, woods and houses receded until the altimeter read a thousand feet. At this height the climb ceased, and the machine flew onwards at a steady 95 mph. I saw several large woods, the existence of which I had never known before, slip under the wings, seemingly impenetrable.

I had heard that when flying level, the nose of the machine should appear to be just above the horizon, but I failed to notice this as there was so much else to look at. Away in the distance, the Handley Page Aerodrome and hangars could be seen and I thought I could see a Hampden standing there. None of the characteristics of the Hampden were visible at that distance, but I think it must have been one as there are hardly any other planes at the Radlett Aerodrome. A train puffed slowly along a line which looked as if it were at the same level as the surrounding countryside, though actually I knew it was on a high embankment.

Suddenly the port wing dropped and the starboard wing-tip seemed to sweep around the horizon, and I felt the same sensation as one feels on a "switchback", though in a lesser degree. I remember feeling a tendency to slip over to the lower side of the cabin. I suppose the bank was not very steep but it seemed steep enough for me. We straightened out and headed for St. Albans.

A large 22-seater Albatross outside the de Havilland building looked like a "Dinky Toy" model, while the aerodrome itself did not look any too large to put a plane down on.

All the countryside looked flat and I realised how many lanes there were that I had never been along. Woodcock Hill, which is a cyclist's nightmare, was apparently a flat, winding road, leading to a half-finished building – the new wireless station. In a short while we were over St. Albans, and I at last picked out my house, the

19

yellowy roof being the main indication as to which it was. The puddles in Beech Road resembled little pools of silver paint, carelessly spilled. Another bank and we headed back again to Hatfield, passing over my school (I could see right down into the quad).

It soon began to rain and then an indication of the speed of the plane, the only one apart from the air-speed indicator, was visible in the way the raindrops ran quickly back into long thin lines on contact with the glass of the windows.

As we glided in to land, I resolved to see the landing speed on the air-speed indicator but forgot as the grass, fences and fields, which seemed to flash backwards, took all my attention. At the actual touch-down, I was too busy looking at the fleeting grass to notice what the speed was.

I had been told that landing gave one a terrible feeling, that the earth was rushing up to hit the machine, but I don't remember experiencing any such feeling. I think it must need a very vivid imagination to visualise this rushing up of the ground.

As we touched down, the bumps started again in contrast to the smooth passage through the air. There was a curious half-deaf feeling in my ears but I was told to pinch my nose, close my mouth and blow in order to stop this, and it was very effective.

I didn't realise until afterwards that the scenery from the air had appeared just as I had imagined it would, and so had the landing and take-off. In spite of this, I enjoyed the flight greatly and shall always remember it.

This article uses the diaries of Ben French to tell the story of Germany's pre-war photography of potential English bombing targets. It was published by Hatfield Local History Society in its September 2012 (Issue 86) newsletter.

IN the year before the outbreak of WW2, Ben French was a trainee ground engineer at the de Havilland Aerodrome. His job was to service aircraft engines and approve them for flight. One winter's day he saw a German civil aircraft pass over the de Havilland site and recorded the event in his diary on Wednesday 19th January, 1938. His entry read: "Junkers machine circled Hatfield."

Junkers Ju 52

Ben also noted the plane's identification. It was a three-engine Junkers Ju 52 which had suspiciously veered from its Berlin-to-Croydon Aerodrome flight path to take "snaps" over Hatfield. In the uncertain times that led to war, the Germans had begun compiling an aerial photographic map of Britain to help their pilots identify targets in the event of hostilities – and the de Havilland Aircraft Company was certainly one of them. These photos became known as "Hitler's holiday snaps". At the time, Germany

21

was well ahead of Britain with this type of reconnaissance. At least two photographs of Hatfield were taken and, incredibly, Ben French saw them do it.

Ben noted:

"The Junkers airliner flew over Hatfield. A DH 91 Albatross standing on the aerodrome was quickly taken into the hangar. Was this a spy flight?"

One of the photographs from 1938 shows the Hatfield airfield and a clear outline of Smallford's oval speedway track to the west. Vehicular access to the speedway track was in those days gained from the Hatfield to St. Albans Road, sited between what is now Notcutts Garden Centre and Popefield Farm.

Ben French believes that the Junkers aircraft used that day for its reconnaissance over Hatfield was possibly one belonging to Deutsche Lufthansa.

On Thursday 3rd October, 1940 a Junkers Ju 88 of the German Luftwaffe flew low over the de Havilland aircraft factory at Hatfield in bad weather, opened fire and dropped four bombs, killing 21 civilians and injuring many more. This chapter provides edited versions of two eye-witness accounts. The first is by Ron White who was on the airfield that fateful day. The second is by Terry Pole who, while still a schoolboy, located the wreckage of the Junkers plane and, early the following morning, disturbed two soldiers asleep at their posts who were meant to be guarding it.

Ron White's account (written 31st December, 1995)

The morning of October 3rd, 1940 was misty and overcast – a low cloud base of about 500ft.

I worked at de Havillands in the Plant Office as an office boy. Shortly after the morning tea break, I was talking to one of the draughtsmen, heard the noise of an aircraft making a strange sound (German aircraft sounded different to the British), looked up out of the office windows facing the "94 shop" [*originally the assembly shop for the DH 94 Moth Minor*] and saw an aeroplane with German markings flying low over the top of the 94 shop, going from west to east and towards the roof-spotters.

I could see the crew distinctly and shouted out, "It's a Jerry!" All the Plant Office staff rushed to the underground shelter in the space between the Plant and the 94 shop, a distance of about 100 yards. It was still tea-break time for the 94 shop (I'll refer to that later) and there were three men standing by the south face of the

23

94 shop having a smoke, oblivious to the fact that a Jerry had flown a few feet above them. One of the men was my father. As we all rushed down the shelter steps, I gesticulated to my father to follow down. After about a minute we returned to the office at a steady pace.

When I got back, Mr. Pugsley the office manager was phoning the Control. He was unimpressed by the reply he got. We stood around in a group discussing the matter when, all of a sudden, the klaxon blasted off and the urgent voice of Sgt Jimmy James said, "Take cover! Take cover!" We rushed back to the shelter. As the last to enter the shelter were making it down the steps, sounds like machine-gun fire could be heard – then two enormous explosions with vibration, blast and dust. Someone looked out and said the 94 shop was down. I was concerned about my father.

Junkers Ju 88 of the type that bombed the aircraft factory

There were four bombs. I think two bombs exploded simultaneously with the other two, to make two enormous explosions. The next morning, two plant draughtsmen surveyed the site and plotted four craters.

About midday, my father looked into the shelter and said it had been announced that we could all go home and return next morning as usual. There was no canteen – it had been turned into a morgue and dressing station. I walked home with my brother and friends who lived in the Briars Lane / Dellfield Road area and, as we turned the Briars Lane corner by the Misses Caesars' Prep

24

School, it was like a "pit-head scene", the women standing by their doors, looking and hoping.

My brother and I waved to my mother and she went in and started to cook dinner. I was able to tell her that dad was OK – in the sense that he was alive. When he came home, he was badly shaken. When the klaxon sounded, he had been in the lavatory situated on the first floor in the corner of the 94 shop. He found himself blown into the roadway, and then he went about his first-aid duties and carried out the dead.

In the 94 shop there were lots of wooden benches. The extension with its doors to the airfield was sectioned off with small aircraft, and paint and dope – highly inflammable materials. Also, the storage of oxy-acetylene bottles, which exploded in the fire, didn't help matters.

The gutted 94 shop after the bombs exploded

In the year following "Munich" and the outbreak of hostilities, DH had provided dug-out shelters in steel and corrugated iron and covered with earth on the perimeter of their land. Later, reinforced-concrete underground shelters nearer the buildings were built. Also, some 6ft high surface shelters of modified Quetta Bond brickwork and reinforced-concrete roofs were built close to the workshops. Later, it was decided to provide internal shelters where workers could scuttle to when the klaxon sounded; these were shelters of low brick walls with a concrete slab, in the order of 4ft wide x 4ft high. It was one of these shelters that collapsed in the sheet-metal section of the 94 shop. From my memory of the survey, it was almost a direct hit by one of the bombs. Later, after

25

vociferous protests, this type of shelter was strengthened by steel-angle bracing to the external faces and top of the shelter.

I return now to the timing of this bombing. In 1940, the Junkers Ju 88 could fly at 280 mph and that means the plane, after bombing, would have travelled eight miles – the distance to Hertingfordbury – in two minutes.

Now I understand from a local historian that this Junkers Ju 88 crossed the Kent coast at 10.09am in the direction of Reading. This is likely because if one considers the probable route (Kent coast—Reading—Hatfield—a circuit around the outskirts of Hatfield—Hatfield—to crash at Hertingfordbury), the distance travelled at full throttle makes the timing close to 11 o'clock. Besides, as I said before, the Junkers passed over the first time during the last of the morning staggered tea-breaks (say 10.45am).

I have interviewed several men and women on the DH project and everyone that I have taped has given me an accurate account of what they saw that morning and I can't fault them. Also, I've listened to the taped interview of Mr. Pelham (94 shop inspection) and it recalls an exchange of words with me on that morning between the first and second runs of the bomber.

The first time that I saw the Junkers, I would put it at about the height of the concrete chimney (75ft) – there was only one during the war years and camouflaged. I saw the crew very clearly. The plane flew from west to east on the first run-in. It flew west to east on the second run-in; evidence from the taped interviews and its descending crashing mode bear this out. Whether, after the first run-in, it took a left-hand circuit or a right-hand circuit I don't know, but I reckon from the time of the first run-in to the second run-in, that plane must have travelled a 25-mile circuit. Did it take a figure of eight circuit? This might account for some odd direction of sightings.

At the outbreak of war, the aerodrome was defended by four gun emplacements: at Manor Road and Ellenbrook (both on DH land); Briars Lane (at Farmer Hill's field on the 300ft contour);

and near Birchwood Farm. These were Lewis guns and another Lewis gun was on top of the DH administration building roof. In the summer of 1940, the first four were replaced with the latest and most efficient Bofors anti-aircraft guns. The Lewis gun on the office roof ceased to exist and roof-spotters occupied the space. To allow these Bofors guns to operate effectively, trees were cut down; a row at the top of Briars Lane along the dog-leg part (tall poplars) were cut down at Ellenbrook (none exists to-day, but gave the name to Poplars Estate) and this allowed a good arc of fire. I believe all these guns were under the command of an Officer Commanding stationed at the Manor Road site. These guns provided a defence of DH from the north, south, east and west. I believe all these guns opened fire on the second run-in of the Junkers Ju 88. Any of these guns could have hit it and downed it.

Terry Pole's account (written 31st December, 1995)

This is an edited version of an article written by Terry Pole in response to a letter in the local press requesting information on the 1940 bombing. The article was published by the Engineering Management Services (EMS) arm of British Aerospace in its June 1987 newsletter.

This is an account of the little I know of the matter, and it is only a little, mainly thanks to wartime secrecy, for no one would discuss anything remotely related to aircraft production – especially not to a small boy – the time being 3rd October, 1940. I was twelve years old and an ATC Cadet, and consequently keen on aircraft recognition.

At about midday in Hertford, I identified, with considerable awe, a lone Junkers Ju 88 twin-engine bomber. Little could I have realised that, by early the following morning, I would be inside its cockpit!

Although eight miles from Hatfield, I felt earth tremors and heard distant explosions. I wished I could have seen what was happening and thought of the huge drums of cellulose dope I had spotted on the front lawns at de Havillands. I recalled, when on a St. Albans bus, the strong "pear-drops" smell which I can only suppose permeated the entire works then. The de Havilland people and their wooden aircraft did seem a soft and vulnerable target. I just hoped that this particular Jerry was a poor bomb-aimer and kept my fingers crossed.

It has since been recorded that the low-flying Ju 88 had gone across Hatfield northward and returned along the railway line from Stevenage and bounced four bombs onto the wet grass, so that they lobbed up and into the old 94 shop; it was then a busy sheet-metal shop and a good many apprentices were there. Some people were in shelters; others making for them were blasted down the steps.

On the small-boy grapevine later that day, I learned that the raider had been hit by anti-aircraft fire and had crash-landed at Cole Green [*near Hertingfordbury*] about 4 miles from Hatfield. That evening I cycled to Cole Green and from the directions I had been given, and also following the route being taken by an unusual number of people for the area, located the wreckage which was under guard in a pasture.

No one was allowed to enter. Hoping to obtain a closer view I decided, now the location had been pinpointed, to make a visit at dawn on the following morning.

In the early light at 6.30am, the Junkers' remains seemed completely abandoned – not a soul! I observed the complete undercarriage some 30 yards or so from the main airframe and also a bent-back propeller. I slowly walked around the wrecked aircraft, now flat on the ground with its tail-plane level about two feet above the grass. Protruding beyond the end of the right-hand tail-plane were two pairs of British Army boots, and closer inspection proved them to be attached to sleeping soldiers, fitting very neatly under their makeshift shelter! One of them woke up and very anxiously asked me the time. I told him and he said it was lucky for them that I had arrived so early because they were expecting an officer at 7am with their replacements, and sleeping on guard-duty was a court-martial offence. He carried on, "You can look over the aircraft while we get cleaned up, but do not take anything without showing me first."

Such a privilege! The entire canopy was missing and may have been jettisoned, so I climbed into the shattered cockpit.

The first thing I noticed (even without the canopy) was the appalling chemical smell, and I am aware that older aircraft and modern gliders have distinct interior aromas which depend mostly on whether they are built from traditional or composite materials. These aromas usually add something to the character of an aircraft. With years of hindsight, I now think that this particular Ju 88's pungency marked the dawn of the plastic age, the smell coming from an "ersatz" for natural rubber (used for cable insulation etc.) not completely cured and still producing

Junkers Ju 88 shot down after the bombing

fumes – very unpleasant for the crew. [*It could also have come from the "plastic" stiffening members then being introduced on certain German aircraft.*]

After a few movements on the one control column with its shielded firing-buttons, it came completely away as an assembly from the shattered floor. I held it aloft with frayed and broken cables hanging from its base. The guard thought that I wanted it as a souvenir and shook his head. However, parts of the aircraft were obtained as souvenirs and survive today. They are now on display in the de Havilland Museum – the old Stag Lane wooden hut, located adjacent to the Marketing Display centre. [*More recently moved to the Imperial War Museum, Duxford.*]

I asked the guard if he knew whether the crew had survived. He said, "Yes," but that they had been free for some hours before eventual capture by the Home Guard and, although the pilot had a pistol, he had surrendered quietly. It was found he could speak good English.

A broken-open canister of incendiary bombs of the flat-nosed non-explosive type lay in the centre fuselage and, bearing in mind the "pear-drops" fumes at Hatfield, it must be entirely thanks to the accuracy of the Bofors gun team that this worser weapon had not been used. Later, and presumably in a bid to divert similar raids, a dummy airfield, complete with hangars and aircraft constructed from wooden frames and painted canvas, was created at Panshanger.

Soldier guarding the wreckage

With the loss of the aircraft and the crew in a British prisoner-of-war camp and having been prevented from dropping the lethal incendiary bombs, the raid from the Luftwaffe standpoint was only a partial success – an exploit of courage and daring nevertheless, and I wonder if any or all of the crew are still alive and kicking. If so, would they consider a revisit to Hatfield under rather different circumstances?

The late Stan Clayton worked for de Havilland for over 50 years, starting there in the 1930s and not retiring until 1987. During his retirement, Stan Clayton committed his de Havilland recollections to paper, including those of that fateful day in 1940 when the airfield was bombed. The following is an edited version of Stan Clayton's recollections which he wrote down in June 1991.

I STARTED work with Rumbolds in 1936. They fitted the upholstery to the aircraft manufactured at the Hatfield plant, having first made it from patterns in their own factory in London. I only worked for them for approximately six months when I left and joined de Havillands as a shop boy and still only 14 years old. The first aircraft I worked on was the DH 91 Albatross. The area of the

Prototype DH 91 Albatross, G-AEVV, Sept 1938
(with assembly shop in the background and canteen behind)

factory was experimental and the section I was involved in was the sheet-metal shop where I spent most of my working life, apart from a short time on production work. Then, in 1968, I joined the

31

Inspection Department and finished my working life as a Deputy Superintendent Inspector until I retired in 1987.

When we were kids, the London Flying Club was still in operation. They had a swimming pool at the back of the squash courts above which was housed the searchlight which went round and round year after year. The DH employees were allowed to use the pool two evenings a week. We used to think that these rich Flying Club people did not like the idea of using the same water as us because the water was always changed after our second evening.

London Flying Club (with swimming pool visible and the squash courts on the left)

Prior to the 1939 war, two of our directors, Mr. Hearle and Mr. Nixon, gave the boys of the company a building which consisted of four walls, a roof and a front door. There were some very high windows plus an open, but in working order, toilet. They also gave us three sets of wood-working tools and a considerable amount of plywood which had been cut to size for wings of the Don trainer – an aircraft which did not turn out to be very successful. We were told to make ourselves a club which would be known as the de Havilland Boys' Club. We were also given a warden. Our first job at his request was to build an office for him. The second job was to cover in the "loo" to give ourselves a little privacy. The next was a soft-drinks bar, with the emphasis on the "soft". We made a very large table which was used for different table activities. We were given some second-hand chairs which were a big help. The oldest of us would only have been about 17 but we spent a considerable amount of time meeting and working in our club. We later invited girls in. We were trained by men working in the factory in sporting activities such as football, cricket, fencing and boxing; there were always men who were prepared to stay in the evening to assist us when they could.

During the early part of the war our club was taken off us, extended, refurbished and changed into the de Havilland Sports and Social Club – which is still in the same place today. The reason for this was the original men's club was on the top floor of the canteen and to continue using it would have meant going through the main gate into the factory – not good for security during war-time.

Let me ask how many people can still remember the brass disc? It was used when you wanted to go to the toilet. Before you were allowed into a cubicle, you were given a disc. The number stamped on it was recorded along with your name. You were allowed seven minutes to do what you wanted, which usually included illegal smoking so long as you didn't allow the smoke to show over the top of the cubicle. If you were over the seven minutes, you would be reported to your head of department.

On 3rd October, 1940, de Havilland was bombed by a Junkers Ju 88. The sheet-metal shop took the full force of the five bombs [*official records say four bombs*] which fell onto the grass and then bounced into the department, killing in excess of 20 sheet-metal workers. This was my department but I was not in the shop at the time and, on returning a few minutes later, I was confronted by the whole department completely destroyed and on fire from end to end. There was only a small part left standing; that was the upstairs toilet and downstairs cloakroom which had been reinforced. Some men and boys survived the blast by being in the downstairs area. At the back of the shop was a large store in which a considerable amount of metal called Electron was kept. This metal, when it got to a certain heat, would ignite and then, if water was added, as happened from the firemen's hoses, provided a spectacular display like a big firework show. The surface shelters inside the

33

department were death traps because the bombs had blown the walls away – and down came the concrete roof on top of any person who went into them.

My most vivid recollection of that day was seeing two sheet-metal workers, Lofty Cochrane and Butch Lewis looking around the department and picking up pieces of bodies and putting them into black sacks. Only a few minutes before, they had been working alongside the same chaps who were killed.

There were reasons why a good many of us considered that a lot of the deaths were unnecessary. For some time before the bombs were dropped, people living in Hatfield were phoning the de Havilland police box asking why the klaxon had not been blown since a German aircraft was flying over the factory. A friend of mine, Alan Stewart, then a painter in the plant department, was working on the roof and came down quite quickly and notified the police box of what he had seen. But still no klaxon, until the aircraft started to machine gun the airfield, and then there was very little time to evacuate the factory or the sheet-metal shop before the bombs were dropped.

I feel certain that had the crowd, or you could say "mob", got hold of the person who we considered responsible for not blowing the klaxon, I hate to think what would have happened to him had he not been protected by the civil police.

After the deaths, the sheet-metal workers in the factory, who numbered around 200 men, made themselves responsible for the upkeep and maintenance of the grave in St.

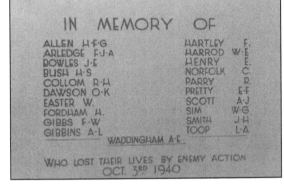

IN MEMORY OF

ALLEN H·F·G   HARTLEY   F.
ARLEDGE F·J·A   HARROD   W·E
BOWLES J·E   HENRY   E.
BUSH H·S   NORFOLK   C.
COLLOM R·H   PARRY   R.
DAWSON O·K   PRETTY   E·F
EASTER W.   SCOTT   A·J
FORDHAM H.   SIM   W·G
GIBBS F·W   SMITH   J·H
GIBBINS A·L   TOOP   L·A
WADDINGHAM A·E

WHO LOST THEIR LIVES BY ENEMY ACTION
OCT. 3RD 1940

Plaque in memory of the 21 who lost their lives

34

Luke's graveyard, which I am sorry to say is in very poor condition today as there is no longer the same number of men – at the time of writing [*June 1991*] only 20 in total.

Times have changed and not for the better. Shortly after that terrible day, whole departments were dispersed. Sheet Metal was sent to Unity Heating Factory in Broadwater Road, Welwyn Garden City and the fitting shop took over two factories in the same road. Woodworkers went to a factory known as Woodfield Road No. 1 and the Machine Shop went to St. Albans.

When we consider the number of great aircraft designed and manufactured in Hatfield, we should all feel justly proud of the expertise of the whole de Havilland workforce. There was very little help from Hawker Siddeley Aviation – and British Aerospace was not a lot better, even though they were in control for much longer than Hawkers. With all the rumours and known redundancies at the time of writing [*June 1991*], there seems little hope now of any new planes. I think it is a shame but that is what business is all about these days: "Money!". They can get more by selling off their assets than they can by making aircraft.

I suppose I must come to accept that things don't always stay as you would like them too. But I am like Blackpool Rock, I have de Havillands right through me. "And proud of it!"

Postscript

Since Stan Clayton wrote these memoirs, the airfield has been redeveloped into a business park and housing estate. The de Havilland Sports & Social Club, originally on the Hatfield Garden Village side of the airfield, was relocated to the University of Hertfordshire's de Havilland Campus, St. Albans Road West. The new building was opened in March 2002 by Lord Maclaurin, the then Chancellor of the University. In 2007 the club was renamed "Club de Havilland".

Hatfield Local Defence Force, 1939

Eddie Chapman was a wartime German spy who then became a double-agent working for MI5 under the code-name "Agent Zigzag". This article by Peggy Tomey was published by Hatfield Local History Society in its March 1998 (Issue 28) newsletter.

DROPPED by parachute in December 1942, Eddie Chapman was equipped with a wireless, automatic pistol, cyanide suicide pill and £1,000. Trained in Germany he had been offered £15,000 to blow up the factory producing the Mosquito. On 29th January, 1943 he scaled the factory fence and laid charges around the power plant. The explosion blew off part

Eddie Chapman (Agent Zigzag)

of the roof and pieces of transformer were found scattered around the area. The action was reported in national newspapers at the time and Chapman's Abwehr controllers sent him congratulations.

Unknown to the Germans, when he landed he had surrendered to MI5 and offered to work for the British. The explosions at Hatfield were a hoax made to appear a far more serious attack. They were planned by MI5 with the assistance of the celebrated illusionist Jasper Maskeleyne. Chapman had been arrested in 1939 for safe blowing in Glasgow but had escaped to Jersey where he was apprehended. While awaiting return to Scotland, the Germans occupied the Channel Islands and recruited him for sabotage work. After his exploits in Hatfield he was given assisted passage to Lisbon to enable him to return to Germany. Awarded the Iron Cross, he was sent back to Britain on another mission in 1944 but again surrendered. Due to his involvement with the criminal fraternity, MI5 dispensed with his services.

More "Goings On" at the Aircraft Factory

The above article jogged Ron White's memory about other mysterious matters. This article was published by Hatfield Local History Society in its September 1998 (Issue 30) newsletter.

A T the time of the events reported above, I was working in the Plant Office and there was no suspicion of sabotage. Power was maintained, backed up by an alternative supply. Repairs, reinstallation and clearing up of debris were carried out without delay. Subsequently I learned of the existence of a contingent of Poles, secretly housed in the top floor rooms of the parade of shops opposite de Havilland's main gate. They were being trained for infiltration and sabotage of industrial works in enemy occupied Europe. Some succeeded in entering DH's works.

The Power House superintendent, Charles Trethewey, verified that visiting cards attached to 'notional bombs' from the Poles had been found in the areas of the Power and Boiler House. The real event that caused a flap was the theft of a general arrangement drawing of the Mosquito, still on the secret list, about the end of September.

In October, the BBC announced the existence of the "wooden wonder" [*nickname of the DH 98 Mosquito*]. The drawing was never returned or found. Speculation was that it was on its way to Germany, but one wonders if a Polish saboteur on his own initiative had lifted this secret drawing.

38

This article was written by Daphne Hickson and published by Hatfield Local History Society in its September 2007 (Issue 66) newsletter.

I WAS still at school when WWII started, but on leaving I obtained a job in the Mailing Department of the de Havilland Aircraft Co. Ltd. There were five of us teenagers and we each had a "Round" to do – about four times a day. This consisted of delivering the mail, memos, notes, small parcels etc. to the various departments throughout the Company and also collecting same to be delivered to other departments.

My round included the Restaurants, First Aid Department and the Service Department. The Service Department round included the Air Transport Auxiliary Women's Team which was stationed there. These ATA women

ATA Women Ferry Pilots in World War II

were taken on as Ferry Pilots (replacing men pilots who had joined the Forces). I believe there were about eight of them and in charge

39

AUSTRALIA IN 20 DAYS!
Miss AMY JOHNSON'S
AMAZING SOLO FLIGHT
in a D. H. GIPSY MOTH!
(Standard, except for extra tankage)

This English heroine of the air, the only
girl to hold an Air Ministry Ground
Engineer's Certificate, chose Wakefield
CASTROL XXL for her daring flight across
deserts, jungles and miles of open sea.

using · · · **WAKEFIELD**

CASTROL XXL

The Product of an ALL-BRITISH Firm, recommended by the De Havilland Aircraft Co. Ltd.

C. C. WAKEFIELD & CO., LTD., Wakefield House, Cheapside, London, E.C.2

40

of the group was Pauline Gower. They were all qualified flying instructors and had several years flying experience. Their jobs were to deliver small aircraft from factories to various squadrons and stores in the UK and also to ferry members of de Havilland to other aircraft factories, including our Chester Branch. Amongst the ATA women was Amy Johnson, a very nice person who always greeted me with a smile when I handed over her mail.

After a few months in the Mailing Department, I was transferred to the Buying Department as a copy typist, mainly typing purchase orders for all the items needed for an aircraft factory, from nuts, bolts and screws to the fabric and dope needed for the structure of the aircraft wings. This Dope Department was manned mainly by women.

Many women in the vicinity of Hatfield who had no home ties were asked to help the war effort by joining de Havilland and some were allowed and able to make parts for the Mosquito aircraft in small sheds and back yards. This was most useful in terms of security as this method of construction prevented the possibility of production being stopped by the enemy.

De Havilland had many sporting teams; I joined the Ladies Keep Fit Team and we had about 30 members at one time. We all loved the classes taken by Eileen Fowler. Eileen taught keep-fit classes at many other large firms employing women in Welwyn Garden City and Hatfield. They included the Shredded Wheat Factory, Norton Grinding Wheels,

Ladies Keep Fit Display, Hatfield sports field, 1951

Roche Products, Nivea Cream Factory and the Box Factory in

41

Hatfield. Each year, Eileen would give a massed Keep Fit Display in Welwyn Garden City on the Campus and one year she had over 120 girls all performing exercises.

In 1949, I left de Havillands to get married and moved away to Barnet, but two years later I was phoned and asked if I would like to return and do part-time work. I agreed and was employed in the Sales Department – most interesting. Later that year I was allocated a flat in Hatfield and asked to do full-time work as Secretary to the Chief Accountant. Shortly after this, DH was taken over by Hawker Siddeley Aircraft and the original directors of de Havilland were moved to Great Nast Hyde House with the Company Secretary and Chief Accountant. Although I was sad at leaving the Aircraft Company again, working with the directors was most interesting. Just before I left Great Nast Hyde House to have a baby, I was asked to "stand in" for Sir Geoffrey de Havilland's secretary who was ill, which I did. So, I started in the lowest department for girls and ended my career working for the man at the top – Sir Geoffrey de Havilland.

ATA Briefing - Women Ferry Pilots in World War II

Chapter 10   Memories of a First Jet Plane (1945)

This letter from Ernest Kohn of Abingdon was published by Hatfield Local History Society in its December 2005 (Issue 59) newsletter.

YOUR September newsletter was passed on to me by a local acquaintance, Mr. George Relph. I found Ms. Laurence's article most interesting, because I had been there [*Bush Hall*]. I was in Shenley military hospital at the end of the war with pneumonia. In the Spring of 1945, I was sent to Bush Hall for two weeks convalescence. I remember a mellow building with lovely grounds, but I don't remember a stream.

The stay was memorable, because while there I saw my first jet plane. It was a de Havilland twin-boom Vampire. As this

DH 100 Vampire

whistled overhead, I stared up in amazement. When I looked down again, I realised that I was on my own – all the battle hardened soldiers had flattened themselves to the ground at the first sound of a penetrating whistle overhead!

With best wishes to your Society.

43

London Flying Club's navigation beacon c.1934

The beacon at its new home, 2013

Hatfield's former London Flying Club beacon is believed to be the only-pre-WW2 beacon still in existence. This article about the beacon was written by Terry Pankhurst and published by Hatfield Local History Society in its September 2006 (Issue 62) newsletter.

IN the early days of flying, there were no navigational aids. Pilots flew by looking out over the sides of the cockpit and following roads and railway lines with a map strapped to their knee. By day these visual landmarks were fine but, as nightfall approached, it was best to find your airfield and land quickly. Various schemes were tried. In 1919, the USA had experimented with bonfires, as I am sure we did. The bonfires were the first artificial beacons to help night navigation. Fires were lit by Post Office staff, farmers and the public – not the most satisfactory arrangement, you must agree. By 1923, lighted airport boundaries, spot-lit windsocks and rotating beacons on towers had taken hold.

Within a few months of moving to Hatfield, de Havilland had built a new club house, squash courts and swimming pool. On top of the squash courts stood the new navigation beacon [*see picture top left*]. Or was it new?

Even now its origin is uncertain, it may well have come, second-hand, from Croydon airport. The beacon seems to have been operational in 1934. A notice to airmen issued in March that year said, "An aerodrome beacon has been installed in the SE corner of Hatfield Aerodrome. The light is operated nightly for one hour from half-an-hour after sunset and shows a white flashing light of 0.92 seconds duration every five seconds. The range of the beacon in clear weather is approximately 38 miles."

The light seems to have been run on the same lines as coastal lighthouses with the duration and spacing of the flashing light acting as identification. At some stage after the war, some civil aerodromes flashed a Morse identity in green and military airfields in red. Aircraft flying in darkness could identify their position from the Morse code. Heathrow certainly had a flashing green light. It was removed after some of the local residents objected to the flashing green light which kept them awake at night.

Hatfield Aerodrome was only a nine-to-five operation other than for emergencies. Therefore it may not have been necessary to have a Morse signal other than for "after hours" operation and then only on request. Even now, opinion is divided as to whether it was green and white or just a white light. I am sure someone will tell me.

The navigation beacon stood in the centre of the British Aerospace site, a lasting symbol of its past history. What a story it could tell, from the days of the Moth aircraft through the war years and the Mosquito production. It stood close to the 94 shop and would have felt the blast from the bombs that devastated that department. It watched over the development of the world's first jet airliner and the troubles it brought. Not a hundred yards away, it would have seen the building of the British nuclear deterrent, the first stage rocket of Blue Streak. It would have been viewed by the many Chinese visitors who came to buy and learn to fly and operate the Trident. It would have watched over the final phase of the site, with the development of the business jet, the 125, and finally the 146 passenger jet.

The dome which topped the building so proudly was removed in 1988 to make a new sales centre. The dome was rescued and put on a lorry – destination Salisbury Hall and the de Havilland Heritage Centre. It clearly did not want to leave because it fell off the lorry as it left the factory gate and was damaged. Lack of space prevented it remaining at Salisbury Hall and it moved on to North Weald airfield and became just another small part of Hatfield's heritage quietly rusting away.

The old de Havilland site, as we know, is now given over to housing. As a well-known feature of that site, the navigation beacon may return and form the centre piece of an art work depicting the historic nature of the once innovative aircraft site. Quite what it will look like and how it will be set as a work of art is yet to be decided. I understand the University's art department is working on designs.

The removal of the beacon in 1988

Postscript

With help from the Heritage Lottery Fund and support from the University of Hertfordshire, the beacon has now been returned to Hatfield. After refurbishment it was installed near the Law Courts Building on the de Havilland Campus, this being the start of the "Hatfield Aerodrome Heritage Trail". It was switched on at 8pm on the 27th September 2013 by local MP Grant Shapps. It is a fitting monument to Hatfield's aviation history.

MOSQUITO
Fastest Aircraft in
Service in the World

Another triumph by

DE HAVILLAND
Leading Builders of Transport Aircraft
in the British Empire

de Havilland Aircraft   de Havilland Engines
de Havilland Propellers   Components and
Accessories   Light Alloy Engineering
Flying Training   Technical Education

In the attack today – on the trade routes of the future

Chapter 12   Geoffrey de Havilland Jnr, Test Pilot

This article was written by Dick Whittingham and published by Hatfield Local History Society in its March 2009 (Issue 72) newsletter.

I GOT to know Geoffrey de Havilland Jnr quite well during the war years as, from the middle of 1942 until the end of 1945, I carried out daily inspections on the experimental aircraft that he flew and signed them out as being safe for flight. This was a great responsibility and privilege as I was only 22 years old when I was first assigned to this position. The first time that I had the opportunity to speak to him was on the first day that I had cleared his aircraft for flight. After he landed the Mosquito I asked him if he would be flying it the next day. He replied, "Yes, the crack of dawn." When I told this to the flight-test foreman I said, "Whatever time will that be?" and he said, "Twenty to ten!"

Geoffrey was a brilliant pilot, the ultimate professional, a man of few words, modest, private and unassuming, like his father and also his brother John who was also a test pilot. He was utterly focused on his job and because of that had no time for jokes or small talk with those who worked with him, although I am sure that other pilots and friends who socialised with him in the evenings when he relaxed would have seen another side of his character. He would never blame anyone if mistakes were made, and once when, due to the failure of a ball-race on a Vampire that nearly caused him to crash, I tried to explain to him what had caused the problem, he merely said, "But when will it be ready to fly again?" Very occasionally one would catch a glimpse of his

49

more human side. He had a passion for model steam engines and once said to me, "If you had a model steam engine, would your wife let you start it up in in the kitchen?" I said, "Of course she would," to which he replied, "They won't let me do it at home."

I only saw him get really annoyed on one occasion. He was flying a Mosquito locally when part of the Perspex canopy broke off and his precious hacking jacket which he always wore and stowed behind his seat was sucked out and blew away. He got as many of his pilots as possible into the air and we watched them circling round and round somewhere near the Crooked Chimney [*a public house at Lemsford*] looking for it. It was never found!

In 1942, Geoffrey visited Canada and the USA. This was in order to hand over a Mosquito to the US Army Air Corps and also to test the first Canadian-built Mosquito. Whilst in Toronto he gave demonstrations to the workers there, and it gives one a good insight into his character when reading his report on his time at the Canadian factory when he wrote, "This was my most unpleasant day out there as three speeches were required from me. They were short speeches."

Before leaving Canada, he flew the Mosquito in a demonstration flight over Toronto in aid of a War Bonds sales-drive. He wrote, "This was a truly amusing show to do and one gained a fine impression of speed going well below the tall skyscrapers with 400 mph indicated." He then toured the USA demonstrating the Mosquito to Army and Naval Air Staff who gave him an opportunity to fly many of their aircraft.

It is worth recording a meeting he had with Howard Hughes [*the American business tycoon*]. Geoffrey wrote, "He is at present engaged on the design of, and construction of, a 30,000lb wooden-plastic transport for the Army Air Corps. This plane was to have been the very acme of simplicity in construction, but Hughes was dumfounded when he looked at the Mosquito. Turning to me he [*i.e. Hughes*] said, 'I guess I'm going to give those goddam designers of mine Holy-jeeze.'"

50

"Sure enough the following day there arrived at the field half a dozen long-faced gloomy-looking individuals, members of the Hughes design staff. They enjoyed several hours inspecting the Mosquito and asking questions. In sympathy, Burrell [*Geoffrey's observer*] and I stood them lunch in the fine Glywayo restaurant."

On occasions, I had the opportunity to fly with Geoffrey in the Mosquito. It was always an exhilarating experience. In the air he was always focused on the job in hand and was completely unflappable. Once

Geoffrey de Havilland Jnr

we were diving almost vertically through thick cloud and suddenly broke out into sunlight, just missing a Catalina that was flying past just below the cloud-base. It was so close that I could see the horrified expression on the gunner's face looking at us from his Perspex blister.

Geoffrey was completely unmoved by the incident as if it was nothing unusual. On the ground however, when ready for take-off, he would not move until you assured him that there was no plane about to land on top of us – the Mosquito had no rear-view mirrors!

The only time I saw him enjoy a joke was when he persuaded Ronald Bishop, the chief designer, whom he called "Bish", to get into a Vampire and taxi it around the airfield. Geoffrey had complained of difficulty in steering it on the ground, whilst Bishop had not taken his complaint seriously. When Bishop careered all over the airfield in all sorts of trouble, it made Geoffrey's day!

For some reason he seemed to have a very cool relationship with the Air Ministry, particularly when they sent RAF officers to have a flight in one of his beloved prototypes. On one occasion when an officer was ready to have his first flight in the Vampire, Geoffrey gave him verbal instructions on how to fly it, but when the chap said, "How do I start the engine up again if it dies on me in the air?", Geoffrey just said, "Oh! Dick will tell you" and left him to it. In the event, he did lose the engine in flight and succeeded in starting it again. When he left, Geoffrey came over to me and said, "What did you tell him?"

What I shall always remember him for is when he was about to take the newly-built Vampire jet on one of its first flights. As he was taxiing it out he suddenly stopped, called me over and said, "How is your wife?" He had heard that she was seriously ill in Barnet Hospital. This shows that he had a kind-hearted side which perhaps was not apparent to many people that he worked with.

He lived for flying. He had been taken up for his first flight in his mother's arms in his father's first aircraft that he had built. And sadly it was while flying that he was eventually killed.

Postscript

Geoffrey de Havilland Jnr OBE (1910-46) was de Havilland's Chief Test Pilot and made the maiden flights of the DH 98 Mosquito and the DH 100 Vampire. He died on the evening of 27th September, 1946 whilst carrying out high-speed tests in the DH 108 Swallow prototype jet aircraft TG/306 which broke up over the Thames estuary, the remains of the aircraft being discovered the following day in the mud of Egypt Bay, Gravesend, Kent.

His test-pilot brother John de Havilland (1918-43) also died while testing a de Havilland plane – the DH 98 Mosquito twin-engine fighter and bomber. On 23rd August, 1943, it was in mid-air collision with another Mosquito and, being constructed mostly of wood, broke up in mid-air, the remains being found not far from the airfield in the vicinity of Oaklands.

Chapter 13   Night Flying at Hatfield Aerodrome

This article was written by Ben French and published by Hatfield Local History Society in its September 2010 (Issue 78) newsletter.

IN 1930, the de Havilland School of Flying arrived in Hatfield from Stag Lane, Edgware where it carried on training pilots for the RAF. The aircraft used at that time were DH 9Js and Gipsy Moths.

In 1935 the name changed to No.1 Elementary and Reserve Flying Training School, teaching Short Service Commission and Volunteer Reserve pilots to fly. By 1938, two Hawker Hart dual control trainers, painted yellow, were used for night flying, where circuits and landings were carried out on Friday nights.

At sunset, or after a day's flying had finished, a flare path was laid out using "Gooseneck" flares. These were similar to short oval watering cans with wicks protruding from their large spouts, the cans being filled with paraffin.

An engineer and myself would lay out the flare path. For this we used an old Humber Snipe open car. The rear seat had been removed and we loaded up the space with the cans, then placed them in two lines along the aerodrome (as a runway) wide enough in the middle for the aircraft to take-off and land. Each flare was lit as we placed it in position. We'd then return to the electricians' store to load up with small electric lamps called "Glim Lamps", which were used to define the aerodrome boundary. However, the flare path was illuminated by a "Chance Light" which was positioned to one side (Chance was the company name of the maker).

On standby, in case of emergency, was an ambulance (driven by a qualified first-aider) and a fire truck (driven by an engineer or myself). In retrospect, it was amazing that we were not actually given any formal instructions to operate the fire-fighting equipment, which mainly consisted of several large extinguishers that would discharge foam. Fortunately we never used them.

The Chance Light was a high-power electric lamp and generator mounted on a trailer. When it was switched on, pheasants would wander into its path to feed under its light. But when the aircraft took-off, the birds would take flight and sometimes get caught in the bracing wires of the undercarriage. It was not uncommon to see an instructor searching the path for his Sunday dinner!

Flying usually finished at midnight and there was an agreement with the local Council not to fly after this time. Whatever time we finished, it still took us another hour to pack away the equipment before we could go home. My engineer partner would drive the car along the flare path with me crouched on the car's running board gripping the door. As we came to a flare can, I would grab the handle of the can and push the wick down the spout with a long rod, then place the can in the back of the car. We became so adept at this routine that we never had to stop the car. But one night I had not pushed the wick down far enough and set fire to the back of the car, which we frantically put out.

Sometimes the driver would shout, "Hang on!" and speed after a hare caught in the glare of the headlights. On one occasion we skidded on the wet grass as the hare turned, and we nearly ended up in the Ellenbrook stream. We decided that our type of hare-coursing was too dangerous after that. [*The Ellenbrook stream was later piped under the airfield runway site for about ¼ of a mile, until opened up and channelled again in 2002.*]

Although I was salaried, flat-rate overtime was paid for night flying duties but only between 10pm and 1am. For my three hours work, I would receive 1s 6d but I viewed these unsocial hours as being just part of the job.

The original Harpsfield Hall and Farm, 10th March, 1934

Chapter 14   Farming at de Havilland

This article was written by Jon Brindle and published by Hatfield Local History Society in its December 2010 (Issue 79) newsletter.

IN October 2010, a country park called Ellenbrook Fields was opened on part of the remaining de Havilland airfield site – the southern part between the end of the new Salisbury Village housing estate and the Notcutts garden centre boundary.

Whilst information boards warn [*in 2010*] that the area is destined to become a gravel quarry, there is still a pastoral reminder of the non-aircraft activity that took place on the ex-de Havilland site by the company: Farming. A herd of about a dozen longhorn cattle now graze upon what once was the runway.

As World War II approached, agriculture began to play a significant role at the aerodrome. In 1938, former de Havilland Chairman Alan S. Butler initiated a drive in Hatfield to help feed the country with home-grown produce by restoring uncultivated land owned by the de Havilland company.

He gave this important task to DH's first Agricultural Manager, Reg Sutterby. Reg had joined the company's ground staff in 1933, "to look after a little bit of garden in front of the office block and the grass airfield". This was at a time when farming at de Havilland had not even been contemplated.

The farm was featured in an article entitled "Comet Country" which appeared in the autumn 1952 edition of the Ford Motor Company's magazine. In 1938, Reg Sutterby successfully set

57

about cultivating every odd parcel of land that had previously produced nothing. He dug up playing fields, tennis courts, a golf course, lawns and wasteland.

He had soil samples analysed and had to spread 20 tons of lime per acre to bring the 220 acres of arable land under the plough. Throughout the war, sufficient green vegetables were produced for canteens that catered for over 6,000 people – including enough potatoes for 10 months of the year.

All this valuable contribution to the war effort was achieved by borrowing machinery from neighbouring farmers. Remarkably, permission to buy tractors was denied him during the war because Hatfield was not an "agricultural holding" in the eyes of the Agricultural Executive Committee.

By the early 1950s, Reg Sutterby was farming de Havilland's lands that were once part of the ancient Manors of Great Nast Hyde, Harpsfield Hall and Astwick. In all, 1,400 acres were farmed including 750 under the plough.

The farm in 1952

After the war, livestock began to be introduced. Reg commandeered former RAF huts and disused corrugated steel aircraft hangers for use as barns. A foundation herd of twenty Mayford Friesian heifers was bought – also a prized bull, the son of the 9,000-guinea Dutch Rudolph.

A foundation herd of Wessex Saddleback pigs was also procured which, by 1953, had grown to over a thousand 'fatteners' being fed upon home-grown meal and factory-canteen waste.

Over 4,000 head of poultry – turkeys and a few varieties of chicken – were housed in the old RAF huts with thermostatically controlled heating and lighting installed.

The Ford magazine article noted that agriculture at de Havilland's Hatfield site was operated on strictly commercial lines and "not backed by unlimited support by the parent Company, to which they are a credit." And it concluded, "Complete harmony between the world's oldest industry and one of the newest becomes a reality when one watches the Comets and Venoms speed down the runway between the waving crops of wheat and barley."

The Gun Butts at de Havilland, photographed in 2006

Chapter 15   The Gun Butts at de Havilland

This article was written by Ben French and published by Hatfield Local History Society in its September 2010 (Issue 78) newsletter.

THE gun butts at Round Wood were built in the early days of World War II and were to be ready for testing the .303 Browning machine guns and the 20mm cannons of the prototype Mosquito fighter plane (W4052) which first flew on the 15th May 1941. Five days later the Mosquito was jacked up at the "butts" to simulate its flying position.

Firing started with single shots, building up to longer and longer bursts. After each firing, a stringent inspection was carried out, not only for target alignment but to see if the recoil of the cannons had caused damage to the wooden airframe – an issue the attending Air Ministry gun specialist had concerns about. However, the tests soon dispelled these fears.

Later the gun butts would have been used for the Vampire and Hornet fighters.

There was also a row of three flat-roofed solidly constructed brick buildings in the woods nearby. These had heavy steel doors and were used to store ammunition. [*demolished in 2009*]

Only prototype aircraft were tested in this way. It must be remembered that security was very tight at the time and, unless one was involved with this project, not a lot of people would know what actually went on. Post-war, the butts were possibly used to see how much damage would be caused by bird strikes to the Comet and Trident jet airliners.

Prior to the above, between 1935-9, different brick-wall gun butts had been used for target practice by the trainee pilots of No.1 Elementary and Reserve Flying Training School. Those butts were adjacent to the former Sinclair's farmhouse [*Harpsfield Hall Farm*] and were later to become the de Havilland Engine Company test beds. I was a trainee Ground Engineer at the time and I would be detailed to drive Len Gaskin, the Flying School Armourer, over to the butts where he would level the piled-up sand and strip and clean the .303 Lee Enfield rifles of World War I vintage!

The old farmhouse was derelict but part of an orchard was still there. During the apple season I would fill a box and take it back to the lads in the hangar. The high wall of these butts remained for many years after the war.

In about 1960, other testing was carried out at the Halford Laboratory (Dynamics, Manor Road) site for damage caused to jet engines through bird strikes. Live chickens were delivered to the site. One would be killed and, while still warm, placed in a special gun. The jet engine would be run at maximum revolutions and the chicken was then fired into the front of the engine. The engine would be shut down and then investigations would be carried out to see what damage was done to the compressor blades and engine.

[*A story abounds that the Americans bought into this emerging technology and somebody mistakenly used a frozen chicken, with catastrophic consequences!*]

62

Chapter 16　Hatfield and the Festival of Britain

The Festival of Britain was celebrated in 1951 as a "tonic for the nation". Hatfield's event was held on 23rd June, 1951 but, as reported at the time, proved something of a disappointment despite the presence of Princess Elizabeth and Princess Margaret. The following report appeared in the Herts Advertiser & St. Albans Times (29th June, 1951 edition).

Air Races Cancelled

Princesses among disappointed spectators

The national air races including the Kings Cup race due to be flown from Hatfield Aerodrome on Saturday were cancelled because of bad weather. Among the spectators were Princess Elizabeth and Princess Margaret.

A disappointed crowd of about 10,000 heard the

The two Princesses on the airfield with Gr. Capt. Peter Townsend (left), John "Cat's Eyes" Cunningham (centre) and Lord Brabazon (right)

announcement over the public address equipment after waiting for five hours.

A low cloud ceiling and a visibility limited on the ground to little more than a mile had kept the crowds which commenced to arrive by car, coach, rail and air well before noon in a state of anxious suspense. But they had to wait for more than an hour before anything associated with aviation was provided for their interest. Then they saw some interesting flying by model aircraft in line and radio controlled, among them a miniature of the Brabazon machine.

Only Casualty

In this section the only casualty of the day occurred. A model controlled by radio, after some interesting acrobatics, got beyond control distance and flew off in the direction of Welwyn Garden City. Its loss and request to the finder to return it to the Royal Aero Club were intimated by loudspeaker to the public.

"The great and the good" at the Hatfield event

A demonstration by the Comet was made possible about 3 o'clock; hopes of the crowd began to arise. A helicopter hovered and then manoeuvred over the ground and it was stated that Mr. John Cunningham was to tour the circuit in a Vampire and report upon the visibility over the course.

He returned after a short time and made his report. The crowd however were held in suspense. The Royal Aero Club committee declined to comment itself immediately and while Flying Officer Murphy of No 66 Squadron RAF displayed the capabilities of the Gloster Meteor 8 machine and the *Patrouille d'Etampes*, a famous aerobatic team of the French air force, thrilled the public, constant consultations were going on and weather reports from around the circuit were being received.

Conditions worsened and, anticipating cancellation, large numbers began to leave the field. About 5pm the final decision was taken and the crowd informed that although the races had not been able to take place it did not necessarily mean that they had been abandoned.

The decision rested with the Committee which would meet in a month, but in view of the crowded season it seemed unlikely that the races would be held this year.

Saturday was the first day since the institution of the King's Air Race in 1922 that the race had to be abandoned owing to the weather.

Children's Christmas Party in the upstairs canteen, 13th Jan, 1951

Sports and Family Day on the sports field, 14th July 1951
(with Manor Road houses in the background)

66

Chapter 17 **Post-War Social Life**

This article was written by Albert Jackson who started with de Havilland in 1950 as an apprentice at the de Havilland Aeronautical Technical School at Astwick Manor. After 43 years of service in a variety of technical and managerial positions, Albert looks back at the strength of the social side of the company.

ONE of the features that employees enjoyed and took a great deal of pleasure from was the de Havilland Sports Club. Among the many and varied activities that we enjoyed was the annual Sports and Family Day. Usually held on a Saturday in July, this would see the whole of the sports field marked out with running track and jumping pits.

The afternoon revolved around the various DH departments competing for points to claim the interdepartmental trophy. Many fine athletic performances by employees were achieved. In addition, there were open events which attracted athletes from the local area, even cyclists from local clubs who, one year, raced on the grass track.

As well as serious competitions, there were races for children, ladies and less athletic men. We all enjoyed the fun, especially men rolling the barrel and tilting the water bucket from a wheelbarrow.

Huge crowds of employees, our families and other Hatfield residents cheered every event and applauded the victors collecting their prizes. These were presented, usually, by the directors and were said to be of very good value.

The sports field also had marquees with displays by the photographic club, the art club and the very popular wine-makers club.

In the immediate post-war years, displays by the de Havilland ladies keep-fit class provided an interval attraction and, at other times, there were marching bands or police dogs and their handlers to entertain the crowd. I remember one year there were Cossacks on horseback.

Refreshments were available all day—the marquee being described appropriately as the Beer Tent.

The company arranged for a funfair to be located in the sports field. It was probably the biggest to visit Hatfield. It was open evenings all week and all day Saturday, being well patronised, especially Friday evening and on Saturday, There were the usual rides and sideshows plus a boxing booth where locals were invited to try to beat the fairground boxers. I don't think anyone did.

Another event which employees enjoyed was the children's Christmas Party.

Post-war, with rationing still in being, employees' children could come to a traditional party – in fact, so many came that the upstairs canteen was filled with children for three Saturdays each January. The usual fare was sandwiches, cakes, orange squash and jelly followed by an entertainer. Then, before being collected by their parents, each of them received a present from Father Christmas.

These memories are of the late forties and fifties when employee involvement in social activities was at its peak.

In 1960, de Havilland was taken over by Hawker Siddeley which was later merged into British Aerospace in 1978. After financial difficulties, British Aerospace announced in 1992 that aircraft production at Hatfield would cease from 1993. At the time, Mrs. Berryman, in old age, wrote down her memories of de Havilland and her regret at the impending closure. Here is an edited version of her account which she wrote in October 1992.

These are the personal reflections and recollections of an old woman who lived in Hatfield for 42 years in the same house. We moved to Hatfield in 1937 to live in Hatfield Garden Village at the end of the de Havilland runway. My husband was a Class A tradesman, an engineer pattern-maker who had served a seven-year apprenticeship in the shipyards of the North East coast.

He worked in the pattern shop of the de Havilland Aircraft Co. for most of his 32 years employment; pattern-making has since disappeared and been replaced by a much more modern method.

Life was uncomplicated compared with today's hectic living. Then came the War, which changed everything. In 1942, any woman capable of working had to find a job, so I joined the de Havilland buying office where I stayed for 21 years. There was a wonderful camaraderie during the War and I enjoyed it all, and was very sorry when I had to leave.

My husband joined de Havilland's own Company of Home Guard; they were issued with broom handles at first to repel intruders. I remember him nightly patrolling the perimeter track around the airfield at night and then going in to work as usual next day.

Some bombs fell on Hatfield but the worst fell on the factory, on what was called 94 shop, and some people were killed. The young girl next door was at work there and fled to the underground shelter with other workers. When the bombs fell, the roof of the shelter descended so low that they all had to lie on the floor. The door jammed and they could not get out and had to be dug out – a very dramatic situation for those trapped.

In the early days at Hatfield, the aircraft in production at that time was the Tiger Moth. We would sit in the garden and watch as six or seven of them took off one after another, and we thought they were wonderful as we had hardly ever seen an aircraft where we came from – and we had no perception of the wonderful and strange aircraft that would be flying over our heads in the years to come. Proud to have been a very small part of that great organisation, I remember with pride such aircraft as the Comet, the Trident, the 125, the 146 and the occasional Harrier.

Hatfield continued to prosper for many years, and then friends wrote and told me that the shops were closing and a decline had set in which culminated in the recent news that they have decided to close the factory down.

It had been the bread-and-butter, yes and the jam, for people of Hatfield for a long time and I fail to think what Hatfield will do without it. I am so very sorry to realise that it will be no more.

Chapter 19 The Last Great Picnic (1994)

Friday, 8th April, 1994 was Hatfield's last day as an airfield and a de Havilland Chipmunk was the last plane to take off from it. Four days earlier, on the Easter Monday, "The Last Great Picnic" was held at Hatfield Aerodrome with a service of remembrance and thanksgiving conducted by Rev. Group Captain Donald Wallace, Chaplain to the de Havilland Moth Club.

A poem from the service is perhaps a fitting way to end this book.

There'll Always be a Hatfield
(*Sung to the tune of "There'll always be an England"*)

There'll always be a Hatfield,
Alongside Comet Way,
A famous site; an airfield proud,
Made history in its day.

There'll always be a Hatfield,
Scene of a Tiger's lair,
Mosquitoes made from wood and glue,
The Racing Comet's heir.

There'll always be a Hatfield,
No better place to fly,
Ghosts and Goblins whistling through
Turned heads towards the sky.

There'll always be a Hatfield,
A silence must not fall,
An aerodrome for aeroplanes,
Please, SOMEONE, hear our call.

Anon. Circa 1994

THE WORLD'S BEST COMBINATION OF SPEED, SAFETY & PAYABILITY'

Supplied to
IMPERIAL AIRWAYS LTD.   QANTAS EMPIRE AIRWAYS LTD.
RAILWAY AIR SERVICES LTD.   HOLYMANS AIRWAYS PTY LTD.
CHANNEL ISLANDS AIRWAYS LTD., ETC.

The DE HAVILLAND
Four-Engined EXPRESS AIR LINER

PERFORMANCE—with full load of 2 crew, 10-14 passengers, toilet and baggage compartments,
fuel for 472 miles (760 kms.) in all 4,065 lbs. (1,846 kgs.) of disposable load.
TOP SPEED · · 173 m.p.h. (278.5 kms. per hour).
CLIMB · · · to 5,000 ft. (1,525 metres)—6 minutes
CEILING · · · one engine stopped—13,500 ft. (4,120 metres.)
two · · · · — 4,500 ft. (1,370 · ·)
both engines on
one side stopped— 2,500 ft. (763 · ·)
PRICE
£8,500
(Furniture £390- £500 extra)   RANGE · · · 472 miles (760 kms.), or 788 miles (1,267 kms.)

PRODUCT OF THE DE HAVILLAND AIRCRAFT COMPANY LTD. "BUILDERS OF THE COMET" HATFIELD, ENGLAND.

FOR THE WORLD'S HIGHWAYS
A new level of spaciousness and
comfort in the high-speed liner of
medium capacity.

THE DE HAVILLAND

FLAMINGO
CRUISES AT
OVER 200 M.P.H.

THE DE HAVILLAND AIRCRAFT CO., LTD., HATFIELD AERODROME, HERTFORDSHIRE, ENGLAND

Appendix A Aircraft built at Hatfield

A LL of the following aircraft were built at Hatfield. Models prefixed with "DH" were built by de Havilland. The HS / BAe 146 was built by Hawker Siddeley, later British Aerospace.

Aircraft and Year First Flown		
Model & Name	Description	Year
DH 82 Tiger Moth	Two-seat primary trainer	1931
DH 83 Fox Moth	Small passenger biplane	1932
DH 84 Dragon	Large biplane airliner	1932
DH 85 Leopard Moth	Cabin monoplane, three seats	1933
DH 86 Express	Four-engine airliner based on DH 84	1934
DH 87 Hornet Moth	Light biplane	1934
DH 88 Comet	Twin-engine racing monoplane	1934
DH 89 Dragon Rapide	Twin-engine airliner	1934
DH 82B Queen Bee	radio-controlled target version of DH 82	1935
DH 90 Dragonfly	Twin-engine biplane, five seats	1935
DH 92 Dolphin	Twin-engine airliner, to replace DH 89	1936
DH 91 Albatross	Four-engine airliner, 22 passengers	1937
DH 93 Don	Liaison aircraft	1937
DH 94 Moth Minor	Primary trainer, to replace Moth	1937
DH 95 Flamingo	Twin-engine transport	1938
DH 98 Mosquito	Twin-engine fighter and bomber	1940
DH 100 Vampire	Twin-boom jet fighter	1943
DH 103 Hornet	Twin-engine fighter	1944
DH 104 Dove	Airliner, eight passengers	1945
DH 108 Swallow	Prototype jet aircraft	1946
DH 106 Comet	Jet airliner	1949
DH 112 Venom	Jet fighter	1949
DH 113 Vampire	Night fighter variant	1949
DH 114 Heron	Small airliner	1950
DH 110 Sea Vixen	Naval fighter, two seats	1951
DH 121 Trident	Three engine jet airliner	1962
DH 125 Jet	Twin-engine mid-size corporate jet	1962
HS 146 / BAe 146	Four-jet short-haul regional airliner	1981

From 1937, the Airspeed Oxford (twin-engine bomber trainer) was also built at Hatfield but later moved elsewhere to allow for Mosquito production.

de HAVILLAND
controllable-pitch AIRSCREWS

*in full production for all
engine types and sizes, from*
130 h.p. to 1,700 h.p.

Appendix B Key events by Year

BELOW is a timeline of key events in the history of de Havilland while at Hatfield. The company was originally formed in 1920 in rented sheds located at Stag Lane Aerodrome, Edgware. The migration to Hatfield took place in the early 1930s. For reasons of space, not every event is included here – and the table tends to focus more on the earlier years than the later ones.

De Havilland – Key Events at Hatfield	
Year	Event
1928	de Havilland starts buying farm land at Hatfield
1930	Hatfield Aerodrome constructed with hangars, club house and offices
	The de Havilland School of Flying moves to Hatfield
	First Hatfield resident (Don Lawrence) employed
1931	Elstree Studios films *The Flying Fool* at Hatfield
	Royal Iraq Air Force takes delivery of five DH 60 Gipsy Moths
1932	Stage and Screen Aero Club established at Hatfield
	DH delivers ten DH 60 Gipsy Moths to Egyptian Air Force
1933	Squash courts and open-air "lido" built next to clubhouse
	London Aeroplane Club moves to Hatfield
	King's Cup air race starts and finishes at Hatfield (1933-38)
	Geoffrey de Havilland wins the 1933 race in a DH 85 Leopard Moth
	RAF Reserve Flying Club established at Hatfield
	The de Havilland Service Department moves to Hatfield
	DH purchases further land for expansion purposes
	Housing expands to accommodate increasing DH workforce
1934	Stag Lane sees its last maiden flight of a DH aircraft (DH 86)
	DH sells Stag Lane Aerodrome but retains factory there
	DH builds admin block, canteen and restaurant at Hatfield
	The DH Aeronautical Technical School transfers to Hatfield
	DH 88 Comet Racer wins London to Melbourne air race
	DH takes ownership of London Aeroplane Club
	RAF Reserve Flying Club becomes the RAF Flying Club
	Navigation beacon installed on top of squash courts
	Hatfield sees its first maiden flight of a DH aircraft (DH 80)
1935	Orders for eighty Hornet Moths received in first 10 days
	de Havilland now employing over 1,700 in Hatfield
	London Aeroplane Club celebrates tenth anniversary

de Havilland – Key Events	
Year	**Event**
1935	HRH Prince of Wales becomes patron of London Flying Club
1936	DH 89 Dragon Rapide becomes first aircraft of the King's Flight
1938	John "Cat's Eyes" Cunningham joins DH as a test pilot
	DH 95 Flamingo is de Havilland's first all-metal aircraft
1939	All private flying suspended on outbreak of war
	RAF pilots trained at Hatfield
1940	Maiden flight of DH 98 Mosquito (the "Wooden Wonder")
	First all-women Air Transport Auxiliary (ATA) unit formed
	Amy Johnson is based at Hatfield as ATA delivery pilot
	DH factory bombed with loss of twenty-one lives
	Decoy aerodrome established at Panshangar
	DH 98 Mosquito enters production
1941	DH 98 Mosquito enters service with the RAF
	Amy Johnson dies while on ATA delivery duties
1942	de Havilland produces its first prototype jet engine (the Goblin jet engine)
1943	John de Havilland dies while testing a DH 98 Mosquito
	Maiden flight of DH 100 Vampire (with Goblin jet engine)
1944	Geoffrey de Havilland Snr knighted for services to "war effort"
1945	Geoffrey de Havilland Jnr appointed OBE in King's birthday honours
1946	Geoffrey de Havilland Jnr dies testing a DH 108 Swallow
	John "Cat's Eyes" Cunningham becomes Chief Test Pilot
	de Havilland Propellers incorporated as a Limited Company
	A S Butler gives 90 acres for Hatfield Technical College
	Development of Manor Road site for testing and production
1947	Concrete runways laid for high-performance jet aircraft
	DH 100 Vampire achieves record speed of 496.88 mph
1948	DH 100 Vampire achieves record height of 59,446 ft
1949	First test flight of DH 106 Comet jet airliner
1951	DH takes over Airspeed Ltd (makers of the Airspeed Oxford)
1952	DH 110 Sea Vixen crashes at Farnborough, killing 28 people
	DH 106 Comet enters airline service
1954	First fatal crash of DH106 Comet jet airliner
1955	Sir Geoffrey de Havilland retires
1960	Government cancels Blue Streak ballistic missile project
	De Havilland Aircraft Company taken over by Hawker Siddeley
1963	de Havilland company name discontinued
1965	Sir Geoffrey de Havilland dies at the age of 82

Aircraft production continued at Hatfield with Hawker Siddeley (1960-78) and then British Aerospace (1978-93). The airfield was finally closed in 1994.

Appendix C Airfield Bomb Victims (1940)

TWENTY-ONE people lost their lives on 3rd October, 1940 when a Junkers Ju 88 bombed the de Havilland Aerodrome at Hatfield. Details of those killed come from the Commonwealth War Graves Commission's register of civilian deaths.

Allen, Horace Frederick George—age 37, husband of Gladys Irene Allen, of 9 Broadfield Place, Welwyn Garden City.

Arlidge, Frank Joseph—age 50, husband of Gertrude Grace Arlidge, of 25 Rondini Avenue, Luton, Bedfordshire.

Bowles, Jack Eric—age 26, of 44 Kirwood Avenue, St. Albans, son of Frederick Percy and Sarah Bowles, of 11 Hitchin Road, Upper Caldecote, Biggleswade, Bedfordshire; husband of Elsie Bowles.

Bush, Henry Herbert Stacey—age 35, of 4 Rodney Court, Hatfield, husband of Edith G. Bush.

Collom, Richard Hockley—age 33, son of Mrs. Bowyer (formerly Collom), of Brick Lane, Enfield, Middlesex, and of the late R. H. Collom; husband of V. M. Collom, of 6 Heronswood Road, Welwyn Garden City.

Dawson, Owen Kendall—age 51, husband of Elsie May Dawson, of 10 Heathcote Avenue, Hatfield.

Easter, William James Cuffley—age 24, of 30 Regal Court, Edmonton, Middlesex, son of Mrs. Coe (formerly Easter), of 28 Tilson Road, Tottenham, Middlesex, and of the late G. Easter; husband of V. Easter.

Fordham, Cecil Harry—age 34, of 4 St. Albans Road, Hatfield, husband of Irene Fordham.

Gibbins, Alfred Leonard—age 19, son of Mr. W. A. Gibbins, of 10 Ashley Road, St. Albans.

Gibbs, Frederick William—age 24, of 173 Harringay Road, West Green Road, Tottenham, Middlesex, husband of Irene Gibbs.

Harrod, William Edward—age 49, of 54 Corbyn Street, Finsbury Park, London, husband of Vera Harrod.

Hartley, Frederick—age 27, of 12 Brinkburn Close, Stag Lane, Edgware, Middlesex, husband of Eva Hartley.

Henry, Eric Reginald—age 32, husband of R. Henry, of 3 Roestock Gardens, Colney Heath.

Norfolk, Charles—age 28, of 85 Briar Road, Watford, son of John and Hannah Norfolk, of 34 Manisty Terrace, Easington Colliery, Co. Durham; husband of Doris Elizabeth Norfolk.

Parry, Reginald—age 29, Section Leader, Works Fire Brigade, husband of Nesta A. Parry, of 46 Park View Crescent, New Southgate, Middlesex.

Pretty, Ernest Frederick—age 18, son of A. W. And F. M. Pretty, of 103 Chalfont Road, Edmonton, Middlesex.

Scott, Anthony James—age 19, son of Capt. the Hon. Denys Scott, and Lillis Scott, of The Holt, Appledore, North Devon.

Sim, William James Geddes—age 41, of 17 Selwyn Crescent, Hatfield, son of the late Mr. and Mrs. N. J. Sim, of Huntly, Aberdeenshire

Smith, John Holmes—age 26, son of Lizzie Smith, of 123 Runley Road, Luton, Bedfordshire.

Toop, Lionel Alfred—age 38, husband of A. G. Toop, of 90 Billy Low's Lane, Potter's Bar, Middlesex.

Waddingham, Alfred Edward—age 26, of 13 Mark Avenue, North Chingford, Essex, husband of Hilda Vera Waddingham.

Bibliography

Published Works

"Air Races Cancelled", *Herts Advertiser & St. Albans Times*, June 29th, 1951.

Clark, Fred. "My First Flight", *The de Havilland (Hatfield) Club Magazine*, September, 1939, No. 7.

Lawrence, Don. "The Early Days of de Havilland at Hatfield", Hatfield Local History Society, 2007.

Pole, Terry. "Air Raid on de Havillands 3rd October, 1940", *British Aerospace EMS Newsletter*, June 1987.

Various authors. *Hatfield Local History Society Newsletter*: Mar. 1996 (Issue 20), Mar. 1998 (28), Sep. 1998 (30), Dec. 2005 (59), Sep. 2006 (62), Sep. 2007 (66), Mar. 2009 (72), Sep. 2010 (78), Dec. 2010 (79), Sep. 2012 (86).

Other Items

Anon. "There'll Always be a Hatfield" (poem sung at "The Last Great Picnic", Hatfield Aerodrome, 4th April, 1994), Mill Green Museum (WEWHM: 94/376).

Register of Civilian Deaths. "Deaths in Hatfield Rural District, 3rd October, 1940", Commonwealth War Graves Commission Website.

Berryman, Mrs. "Recollections of 42 years in Hatfield", Mill Green Museum (WHMS: LHF, 4.47 de Havilland).

Clayton, Stan. "Recollections of de Havilland", Mill Green Museum (WEWHM Resource: OHR33).

Jackson, Albert. "Post-War Social Life", previously unpublished.

White, Ron. "Daylight raid on de Havillands in 1940". Mill Green Museum (WEWHM Resource: OHR 98).

Wilson, Abi. "Sir Geoffrey de Havilland, British Aviation Pioneer", "Our Hatfield" Website, 4th March, 2011.

de Havilland airfield and buildings, Hatfield, c.1960

80

INDEX

Note: Page numbers in *italics* indicate photographs;
adv. stands for advertisement.

85

Smith, J. H. 78
Society of British Aircraft
    Constructors 12-13
Spitfire aircraft 12
St. Barbe, Francis *4*
Stag Lane, Edgware *see de*
    Havilland Aircraft
    Company
Stage and Screen Aero / Flying
    Club 9, 75
Stewart, Alan 34
Sutterby, Reg 57-8

T

"There'll Always be a Hatfield"
    (poem) 71, 79
Tomey, Peggy 37-8
Toop, L. A. 78
Townsend, Peter *63*
Tranum, John 10
Trethewey, Charles 38

U

University of Hertfordshire 1, 3, 6,
    35, 47
US Army Air Corps 50

W

Waddingham, A. E. 78
Waight, Bob 13
Walker, Charles C *4*
Wallace, Donald 71
Weedon, Sid 11
White, Ron 23-7, 38, 79
Whittingham, Dick 49-52
Willans & Robinson 5
Wilson, Abi 5-6, 79
Wolseley Tool & Motor Car
    Company 5
women
    Keep Fit classes 41, *41*, 68
    in wartime 41-2, 69
    see also Air Transport
        Auxiliary (ATA)
    see also Johnson, Amy
Woodcock Hill 19
"Wooden Wonder" *see de*
    Havilland aircraft,
    Mosquito [DH 98]
World War II 1, 6, 14-16, 76
    air raids, 23-30, 31, 33-4, 70
    enemy agents 37-9
    Geoffrey de Havilland, Jnr. in
        49-51, 76
    women in 41-2, 69
    see also Air Transport
        Auxiliary (ATA)

#0153 - 140316 - C0 - 210/148/5 - PB - DID1388572